The Stephensons' *Rocket*
A history of a pioneering locomotive

Michael R Bailey and John P Glithero

National Railway Museum
Science Museum

Published 2002 by NMSI Trading Ltd,
National Railway Museum, Leeman Road, York YO2 4XJ.
Science Museum, Exhibition Road, London SW7 2DD.

British Library Cataloguing-in-Publication Data
A catalogue record for this publication is available from the British Library

Designed by Jerry Fowler
Printed in Belgium by Snoeck-Ducaju & Zoon

Additional photography by David Exton, Claire Richardson and Jennie Hills

ISBN 1 900747 49 9

Website http://www.nmsi.ac.uk

Contents

Bibliography

Bailey, M R, 'George Stephenson – locomotive advocate: the background to the Rainhill Trials', *Transactions of the Newcomen Society*, 52 (1980–81), pp171–9

Bailey, M R and Glithero, J P, *The Engineering and History of* Rocket (London: Science Museum/National Railway Museum, 2000)

Burton, A, *The Rainhill Story* (London: 1980)

Dendy Marshall, C F, 'The Rainhill Locomotive Trials of 1829', *Transactions of the Newcomen Society*, 9 (1928–29), pp78–93

Dendy Marshall, C F, *Centenary History of the Liverpool & Manchester Railway* (London: 1930)

Reed, B, *Loco Profile 7: The Rocket* (Windsor: 1972)

Warren, J G H, *A Century of Locomotive Building By Robert Stephenson & Co. 1823-1923* (Newcastle upon Tyne: 1923; republished Newton Abbot: 1970), Chs 12, 13

The Rocket (Darlington: Robert Stephenson & Co., 1929), reprinted from *The Engineer* (31 May 1929)

Foreword

Visitors to the Science Museum's *Making the Modern World* gallery have been greeted by the imposing black outline of the *Rocket* steam locomotive. It is one of the best-known icons in the Museum's collections, and has been on display in South Kensington, almost continuously, since 1862. In 1999, we were privileged to carry out a major survey of the locomotive and its history for the Science Museum and the National Railway Museum. Our survey was both a close examination of all the components, some of which had to be dismantled, and detailed research into all the original documentation relating to its history.

This book is based on the results of this study. It provides an outline description of *Rocket* and its components, and the way in which they worked. It sets the locomotive in its historical context, and emphasises the importance of the father-and-son engineers George and Robert Stephenson. It also describes the fame that *Rocket* achieved in 1829 and its brief career at the very beginning of the main-line railway era.

Readers wishing to understand the locomotive in more detail – its design, materials, manufacture, operation, modification and preservation – may refer to the larger book, *The Engineering and History of* Rocket (ISBN 1 900747 18 9), which is the printed version of our findings from the 1999 survey.

It remains for us to acknowledge the great help provided to us in the preparation of this book. We were aided by several persons connected with the two Museums, particularly Richard Gibbon, Head of Engineering Collections at the National Railway Museum, who managed the study, John Liffen, an Associate Curator at the Science Museum, and Ela Ginalska, the Publications Manager. We should also like to record our thanks to Peter and Robert Davidson of Mobberley, Cheshire, for their invaluable comments on the draft of this book.

Michael R Bailey
John P Glithero

Glossary

Ashbox
A container fitted under the smokebox to collect the fly ash from the coke (Figure 1.10).

Axle
A cross-shaft, with a wheel fitted at each end, which rotated in bearings and supported the weight of the vehicle (Figure 1.18).

Boiler
A cylindrical pressure vessel partly filled with water that was converted to steam (Figure 1.2).

Boiler tube
A tube passing through the boiler, carrying hot gases from the fire to the chimney. *Rocket* had several (Figure 1.2).

Buffing pad
An early form of buffer fitted to both ends of a rail vehicle to absorb shocks from neighbouring vehicles (Figure 1.22).

Coke
Fuel used by early locomotives, made by heating coal in furnaces, leaving a high-carbon smokeless material.

Connecting rod
An iron rod connecting the crosshead with the wheel crank to convert the thrust of the piston into rotary motion (Figure 1.12).

Crank boss
An off-centre extension of the cast-iron wheel nave, into which the crankpin was fitted (Figure 1.17).

Crankpin
A pin fitted to the wheel nave that allowed the wheel to be pushed and pulled by the connecting rod to rotate the wheel (Figure 1.17).

Crosshead
A bronze slide block that linked the piston rod to the connecting rod. It ran between parallel slide bars to maintain the piston alignment (Figure 1.12).

Cylinder
The locomotive's 'engine'. Steam was directed into it, alternately to each end, to push the piston backwards and forwards, providing the motive force (Figure 1.13).

Drawbar
The rigid coupling at the rear of the locomotive that allowed it to draw the tender and the rest of the train (Figure 1.23).

Eccentric
A disc fitted off-centre to the driving axle to provide forward and backward movement of the valve gear to operate the steam valve (Figure 1.24).

Felloe
A segment of the rim of a wooden wheel to which the spokes were fitted. Each was retained in place, with the other felloes, by an iron hoop (Figure 1.18).

Firebox
A copper container attached to the boiler, holding a coke fire and surrounded by a water jacket. The heat radiating from the fire converted the water to steam (Figure 1.7).

Firebox crown
The top part of the firebox.

Firebox saddle
Rocket's 'saddle'-shaped water jacket, forming the sides and crown of the firebox (Figure 1.7).

Footplate
The wrought-iron plate on the rear of the locomotive frame, where the crew stood to drive and fire the locomotive (Figure 1.23).

Keyway
A precise channel cut into a shaft and mating component into which a rectangular 'key' was fitted to prevent movement between them (Figure 1.18).

Leaf spring
A set of bound steel leaves providing sprung suspension, transmitting the weight of the locomotive through the axle box and wheel set (Figure 1.20).

Nave
The centre of a wheel, into which the axle was concentrically fitted (Figure 1.18).

Piston
The close-fitting disc inside the cylinder, pushed by steam alternately from each cylinder end. The thrust from the piston was communicated to the driving wheel (Figure 1.12).

Regulator valve
The throttle valve regulating the flow of steam from the boiler to the cylinders (Figure 1.12).

Rocking shaft
A transverse shaft communicating the reciprocating motion of the valve gear to open and close the steam valves (Figure 1.24).

Slide bars
Parallel bars fitted to the front of the cylinder that restrained the crosshead to a straight-line movement (Figure 1.12).

Smokebox
The chamber bolted to the front of the boiler, through which the used hot gases were drawn and forced up the chimney by the exhaust steam (Figure 1.10).

Steam chest
The chamber above the cylinder through which the steam was alternately distributed to the two ends of the cylinder by the steam valve (Figure 1.15).

Steam pipes
The large-diameter pipes that passed the steam from the regulator valve to the cylinder steam chests (Figure 1.12).

Steam valve
A brass slide valve that controlled the admission of steam to, and exhausting of steam from, the cylinders (Figure 1.14).

Tender
The vehicle coupled behind the locomotive, on which the coke and water were stored (Figure 3.3).

Tube plate
A thick plate riveted into each end of the boiler barrel, between which passed the boiler tubes carrying the hot gases from the firebox to the smokebox (Figure 1.7).

Valve chest
Alternative name for steam chest.

Valve gear
The arrangement of eccentrics, rods and rocking shafts that moved the steam valves at the correct times (Figure 1.24).

Introduction

Rocket is arguably the world's most famous steam locomotive. Railway historians have long recognised it as representing steam technology at the very beginning of the world's main-line railways in 1830. In recognition of this important place in history, its image was incorporated in the design of the Bank of England £5 note introduced in 1990.

The same £5 note also carried a portrait of George Stephenson, the pioneer railway builder. His determination to promote the use of the steam locomotive against sceptical opposition earned him a lasting reputation in railway history. It was, however, his son, Robert Stephenson, who undertook the pioneering development work, in Newcastle upon Tyne. This led to *Rocket* and the many improvements in steam locomotive technology that quickly followed.

Rocket became famous when, just after it was built in 1829, it won a major public competition against three other contenders, demonstrating that it was the best design for railway service. The competitive trials, with a prize of £500, were held near the village of Rainhill, on the route of the world's first main-line railway, between Liverpool and Manchester. The Rainhill Trials attracted much attention and publicity, and many people travelled to the line-side to watch. The crowds correctly anticipated that they were witnessing the very dawn of the new era in travel opportunities that railways would bring.

After the opening of the Liverpool & Manchester Railway in 1830, railway networks grew rapidly in Britain, Europe and North America to provide the means for mass public transport and the movement of goods and minerals. Railways, which now play an important part in the economic and social fabric of most countries, can therefore trace their lineage back to the remarkable work of the Stephensons and their pioneering achievements with locomotives.

Rocket has been seen by generations of visitors to the Science Museum in London since it was first displayed there in 1862. Its simple black outline contrasts with the popular image of its original appearance as a racy-looking locomotive painted yellow, with a white chimney. There is a simple explanation for this contrast. Most machines designed for a long working life need changes, over the years, in their design, materials or methods of manufacture, to improve their reliability and cost-effectiveness. *Rocket* was no exception, and several major improvements were made to it during its working life. Also, many components were removed for their scrap value after the locomotive was withdrawn from service.

To illustrate what *Rocket* looked like when it was first built, several full-size replicas have been made. One of them may often be seen in steam at the National Railway Museum in York, or on its occasional visits to other parts of Britain.

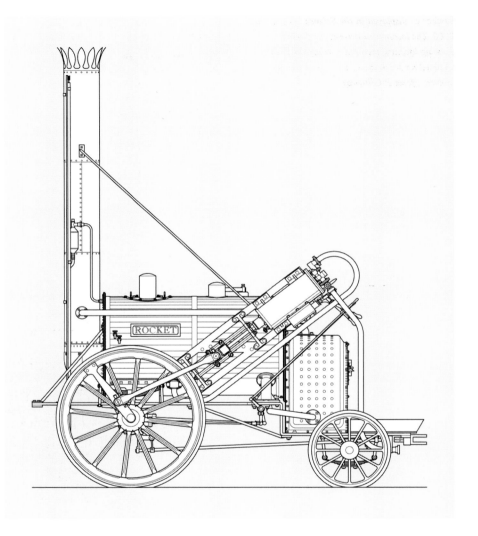

The replica allows us to understand how the locomotive operated when it was first built – and travelling behind it in replica carriages, we can appreciate what it was like to travel on the earliest passenger trains, more than 170 years ago.

This book explores both the reasons for *Rocket*'s success and fame, and its history as the template for future railway locomotives. It also emphasises the tenacity of George Stephenson and the remarkable talents of Robert Stephenson. Their pioneering

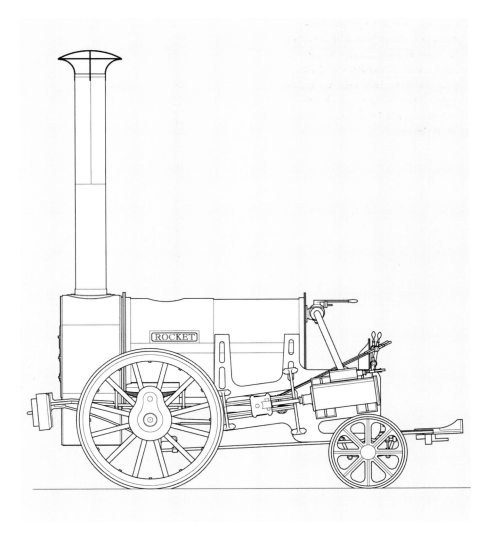

Rocket as displayed in the Science Museum in 2000. The locomotive was rebuilt during its working life, and then many components were removed for scrap after its withdrawal from service. (John P Glithero)

work gave ordinary people the opportunity to travel frequently and extensively. The ease and speed of journeys, and their relative cheapness, attracted large numbers of passengers as the world witnessed the beginning of the mass-travel era. From these origins have grown not only the world's extensive railway networks, but also the extraordinary habit for travel, by train, car, coach and plane, in which most of us participate.

1 How *Rocket* worked

Figure 1.1 Rocket *in the Science Museum's* Making the Modern World *gallery in 2002. The locomotive is in its basic preserved form, lacking its many original fittings. (Science & Society Picture Library)*

Rocket was built at a time when horse-drawn vehicles and sailing ships provided the main forms of transport for people and their goods. Steam power was in its infancy, and the pioneering engineers around Britain were learning how best to harness it to provide a cheaper and more powerful means of moving heavy loads.

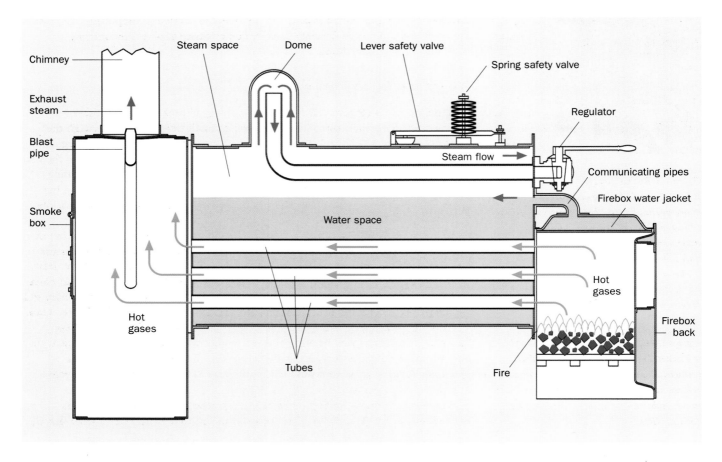

Figure 1.2 To generate steam in Rocket's boiler, a flow of hot gases passed from the fire in the firebox, through the water-filled boiler barrel and into the smokebox, before being ejected up the chimney. (John P Glithero)

Locomotives had gradually developed in the 25 years since the Cornish engineer Richard Trevithick built the first examples. During that time, designs, materials and manufacturing methods had been improved on such pioneering examples as *Puffing Billy*, which is also in the Science Museum's collections, and George Stephenson's engines on the Stockton & Darlington Railway. *Rocket* was, however, a major advance in steam technology, from which subsequent locomotives were derived.

A summary of *Rocket's* components and their functions will illustrate how it converted the latent energy of fossil fuel (coke was the fuel actually used) into a motive force capable of drawing a train of passenger or goods vehicles along a railway line. The locomotive now on display (Figure 1.1) is incomplete, with many components having been removed after its withdrawal from service. It is possible,

Figure 1.3 Rocket*'s original boiler has survived. It is 1830 mm (6 ft) long and 1010 mm in diameter. The 25 copper boiler tubes, each 76 mm (3 in.) in diameter, were constantly immersed in water while the locomotive was in use. The tubes have long since been removed, but the holes in the boiler-end 'tube plates', into which they were fitted, are clearly visible. All the iron stays between the tube plates remain in place. (MRB)*

Figures 1.4–1.6 The lever safety valve as fitted to Rocket. *The valve was first held in place by a weight. This was later replaced by a spring balance fitted to the side of the boiler, which was, in turn, subsequently refitted to the tube plate. (SSPL, NRM)*

however, for the Museum visitor to see not only the surviving components, but also the holes and redundant fitments that provide evidence of where the missing components were once fitted.

1.1 Generating the steam

To generate steam (Figure 1.2), water inside the cylindrical boiler was heated to boiling point. The water surrounded a cluster of small tubes running through the length of the boiler (Figure 1.3), through which passed hot gases from the fire. The surface of the tubes transmitted the heat to generate the steam. This was the first boiler in the world to use multiple tubes. They significantly increased the heating surface area compared to previous locomotives that only had one or two large flue tubes. Steam could be generated much more quickly with *Rocket* than was possible with these previous locomotives.

The more coke that was burnt, the more steam would be generated, resulting in a build-up of steam pressure within *Rocket*'s boiler. The accumulated steam pressure acted to force out the two boiler-end 'tube plates'. To prevent this, several iron stays were inserted through the boiler, and fitted between the plates to hold them in place and prevent them becoming distorted. The boiler was designed to generate steam to a working pressure of $3\frac{1}{2}$ bar (50 lbf/sq. in.). If the pressure exceeded this figure, steam would escape through a 'safety valve' on the top of the boiler (Figures 1.4–1.6). The valve was kept closed by a lever, on the end of which was a weight sufficient to hold in the working pressure. A second safety valve was also fitted as an extra precaution against possible misuse of the weighted valve. Both safety valves were removed many years ago.

The use of multiple heating tubes meant that a separate enclosed 'box' was needed for the fire (Figure 1.7). This box was bolted to the rear of the boiler barrel,

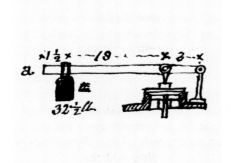

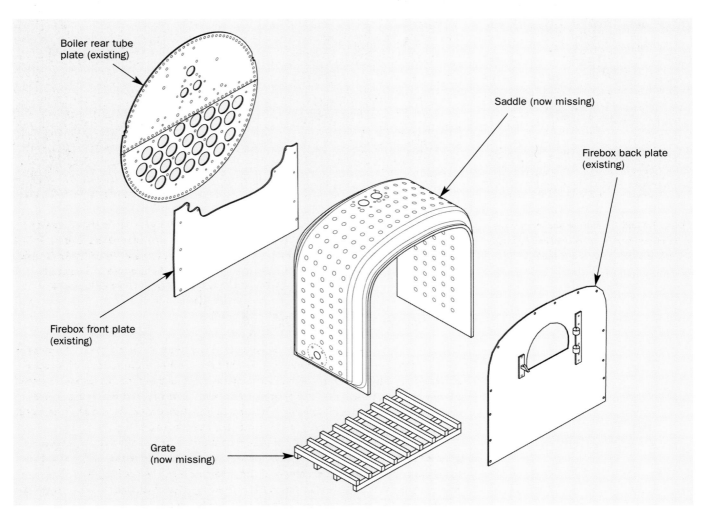

surrounding the end of the tubes. The fire was placed on a grate inside the box. To prevent excessive heat loss from the fire, and to heat the water, a water-filled 'saddle' surrounded the fire on the sides and crown. This saddle, which received heat radiating from the fire, was formed out of two copper plates that conducted heat extremely well. Water was fed into the sides of the saddle through pipes from the bottom of the boiler. The resulting steam passed from the top of the saddle into the rear of the boiler barrel through two communicating pipes.

Figure 1.7 Exploded view of Rocket's *fire 'box'. The copper firebox 'saddle' was removed after the locomotive was withdrawn from service. (John P Glithero)*

Boiler rear tube plate (existing)

Saddle (now missing)

Firebox back plate (existing)

Firebox front plate (existing)

Grate (now missing)

Figures 1.8 and 1.9 Interior and exterior views of the water-filled firebox back plate, showing its fire hole and door. (Michael R Bailey)

A simple plate, protected by firebricks, enclosed the front of the firebox, beneath the tubes. A firebrick-lined plate was also used at first for the rear of the firebox. It had a fire hole and door to allow the fireman to stoke the fire. A water-filled 'jacket', which further increased *Rocket*'s steam-raising ability, replaced the rear plate during its service life (Figures 1.8 and 1.9). This and the original front plate both survive.

1.2 The combustion process

Coke was burnt in *Rocket*'s firebox. This material was specially prepared for locomotive use to avoid producing the smoke that would have resulted from using coal. Smoke fumes would have been environmentally unacceptable at that time. Coke was obtained by heating coal, in specially built ovens, to drive off as many of the impurities and smoke-raising particles as possible. The resulting material had a high carbon content that gave off considerable heat, without smoke, when burnt.

The fire was 'encouraged' to maintain a continuous heat, sufficient to generate a good enough supply of steam. The amount of steam that was required depended on the weight and speed of the trains and the gradients along the railway line. This encouragement of the fire was achieved by drawing a good draught of air through the fire grate that supplied oxygen for improved combustion.

Figure 1.10 The smokebox was fitted on the front of Rocket's *boiler during the locomotive's working life. The hole on the side was a fitting for the exhaust pipe that directed the exhaust steam up the chimney. Ash collected in the box beneath the smokebox and was removed through the small door. (John P Glithero)*

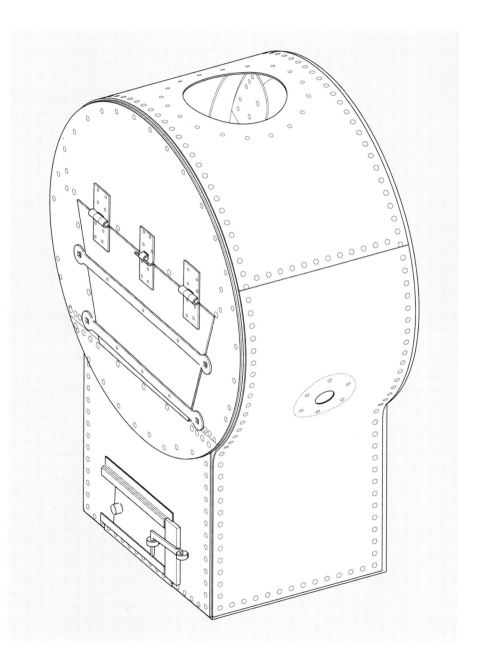

After they passed through the small tubes, the hot gases from the fire were directed up the chimney. The continuous draught of air through the fire grate, and of hot gases through the small tubes, was encouraged by a partial vacuum in the 'smoke-box' at the front of the locomotive (Figure 1.10). To achieve this vacuum while the locomotive was running, the exhaust steam from the cylinders was routed through external pipes along the boiler and turned into the smokebox. The blast of steam up the chimney drew the surrounding air with it to create the partial vacuum. The tall chimney itself also encouraged an upward flow of air to help 'draw' the fire.

1.3 The driving motion

To move *Rocket* and its train, the driver allowed steam to pass in a controlled manner from the upper part of the boiler, through 'steam pipes' to the cylinders, using a cast-bronze regulator valve (Figure 1.11). The steam regulator, on the rear face of the boiler, has a horizontal lever that the driver progressively opened to allow increasing amounts of steam into the cylinders. The original regulator remains fitted to the boiler.

One cast-iron cylinder on each side of the locomotive provided the 'engine' for moving the locomotive and its train (Figure 1.12). Pistons, inside the cylinders, were forced backwards and forwards by the steam pressure. This force overcame the resistance from the friction of all the moving components on the locomotive and the weight of its train.

Figure 1.11 Detail of the rear tube-plate fittings, showing the steam regulator valve and steam pipes. These were fitted just above the twin pipes carrying steam from the top of the firebox saddle into the boiler. The safety-valve spring balance can also be seen in this view. (Alan Stoyel)

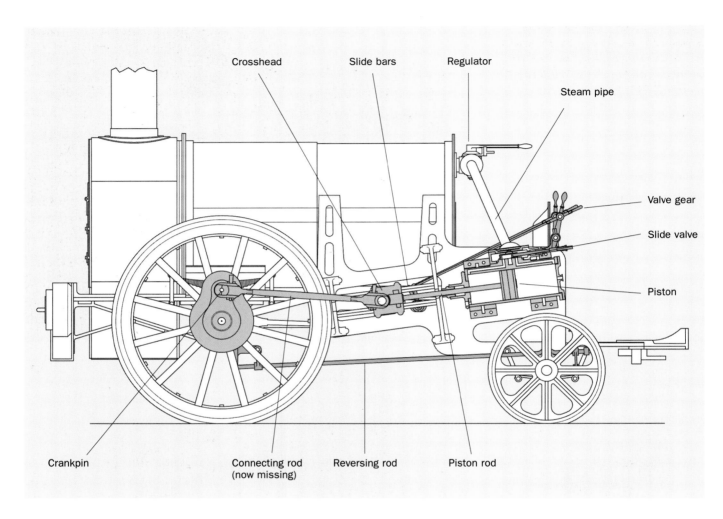

Crosshead Slide bars Regulator

Steam pipe

Valve gear

Slide valve

Piston

Crankpin

Connecting rod
(now missing)

Reversing rod

Piston rod

Figure 1.12 Rocket's *surviving motion arrangement, with the cylinders in a near-horizontal alignment. The force of the steam acting on the pistons was communicated to the wheels via the crossheads and connecting rods.* (*John P Glithero*)

A forwards and backwards 'reciprocating' action was achieved by alternately diverting the steam to each end of the cylinder. This was done by using a sliding valve in a rectangular 'steam chest' just above the cylinder itself (Figures 1.13–1.15). The steam 'ports' were alternately opened and closed by the valve to divert the steam to each end of the cylinder. The valves had a 76-mm (3-in.) reciprocating movement, by a rod mechanism driven from the driving axle.

After pushing the piston, the exhaust steam escaped through the centre valve port. The exhaust steam passed into the space inside the valve and was directed away

Figure 1.13 Rocket's right-hand cylinder surmounted by its valve chest. The piston rod is fitted to the bronze 'crosshead' and the whole assembly is guided by the parallel slide bars. *(Michael R Bailey)*

Figures 1.14 and 1.15 The left-side valve face, showing the steam and exhaust 'ports'. The dismantled valve and 'steam chest' have been inverted to illustrate their form and assembly. (Michael R Bailey)

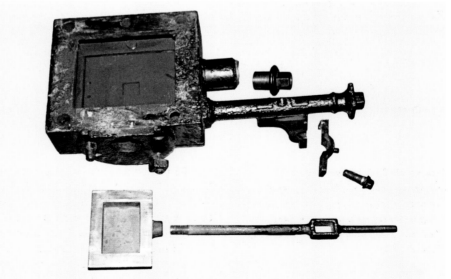

through exhaust pipes. These pipes were routed along the side of the boiler, and into the smokebox before exhausting the steam up the chimney.

The power of the steam pushing the pistons was communicated to the wheels through *Rocket*'s driving 'motion'. Rods attached to the pistons passed through steam-tight glands in the ends of the cylinders, and were fitted at their lower end to cast-bronze 'crossheads'. For the reciprocating movement of the motion, these crossheads were guided between parallel 'slide bars' to maintain an accurate alignment for the pistons. A lot of wear took place on the guide-way surfaces of the crossheads, and occasionally these had to be built up again with brass strips and solder.

Iron connecting rods transmitted the driving force from the crossheads to the driving wheels (Figure 1.16). Under steam pressure, the connecting rods pushed and pulled the crankpins to rotate the wheels. These rods no longer exist on *Rocket*, but the ball-ended crankpins are prominent features on the wheels (Figure 1.17).

Rocket's wooden driving wheels (Figure 1.18) are remarkable survivors from the earliest days of main-line railway operations. Earlier cast-iron wheels were unreliable

Figure 1.16 Rocket*'s driving motion, as drawn during the locomotive's working life. The 'little ends' of the connecting rods were fitted to brass bearings around the crosshead pins. The 'big ends' were similarly fitted around the forged ball-ended 'crankpins' fitted into the wheel naves. (Science & Society Picture Library)*

Figure 1.17 Detail of Rocket's *left-side wooden driving wheel, showing broken and cracked spokes, and the cast-iron crank boss and ball-ended crankpin. (Michael R Bailey)*

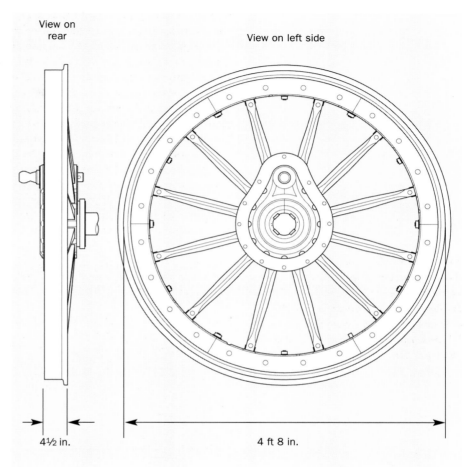

View on rear

View on left side

4½ in.

4 ft 8 in.

Figure 1.18 The left-side wooden driving wheel. The wooden felloes and spokes are hooped with a wrought-iron band and with a flanged tyre. The nave was accurately fitted to the driving axle with four keys. (John P Glithero)

and often broke, and the practice of forging iron spokes had yet to be developed. Wheelwrights, experienced in making wooden wheels for road vehicles and carts, made this set for *Rocket*.

The wheels, which probably date from 1831, have cast-iron naves, incorporating the crankpins. The naves are accurately fitted to the axles by four steel keys, a long-established practice that preceded wheel-fitting with hydraulic presses.

Rocket's smaller 'carrying' wheels at the rear are replacements that were fitted during its time at the Science Museum. The original wheel set was absent at the time the locomotive was being prepared for display in 1862.

1.4 Rocket's frame and assembly

Rocket was first built around a simple, lightweight iron-bar frame, stepped down at the back to accommodate the firebox. The upper part of the frame supported the boiler using four brackets, while the firebox sat on the lower part.

The cylinders were originally bolted to light frames fitted to the side of the boiler at an angle of nearly 40 degrees. This arrangement is the familiar one portrayed on the 1990 £5 note and other images of *Rocket* as first built. The cylinders were later repositioned to the near-horizontal alignment that may now been seen. To achieve this, they were fitted to more substantial rear-mounted plate frames (Figure 1.19). This reduced the downward force on the springs by the piston action that had made *Rocket* unstable in its original form. The alternate, side-to-side deflection of the springs

Figure 1.19 Rocket's frame, showing boiler support brackets, cylinder carrying frames and buffer beam. (John P Glithero)

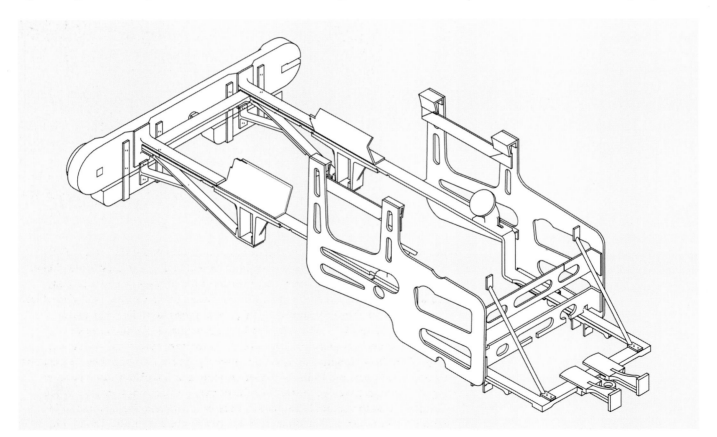

Figure 1.20 Left-side view of Rocket *showing the driving-axle spring behind the driving wheel. The basic design of the locomotive placed more of the weight over the driving axle than over the carrying axle to provide better adhesion. (Science & Society Picture Library)*

produced the unstable ride that, at speed, was uncomfortable for the locomotive's driver and fireman. These large plate frames are braced across the back of the firebox to stiffen up the whole frame assembly, which contributed towards better stability.

The whole weight of the locomotive was transmitted through four sets of steel leaf springs fitted to the frame (Figure 1.20). Two sets transmitted the weight at the leading end of the locomotive through spring pins acting on the driving-axle bearings. The other two sets carried the weight at the rear onto the carrying-axle bearings. With the locomotive in motion, the springs provided some shock absorption from the uneven track and from the thrusting actions of the pistons. Replacement driving-axle springs have been fitted, but the carrying-axle springs are now absent.

The frame also transmitted the tractive force of the locomotive that allowed it to pull the load of a train. The 'drawbar' was fitted to the rear of the frame to be

Figure 1.21 Detail of the buffer beam, showing surviving paintwork. (Michael R Bailey)

Figure 1.22 The left-hand buffer remains, showing the contact plate, backing timber and tail-rod hole. (Michael R Bailey)

coupled to the tender and, through that, to the other vehicles of the train. Buffing pads were also fitted to the rear of the frame, allowing vehicles to be pushed when running backwards. At the front end of the frame, a large oak buffer beam was added during *Rocket*'s operating career (Figure 1.21). This allowed it to pull loads while running tender first, or to push vehicles along the track. A painted 'No. 1' from its days on the Liverpool & Manchester Railway can still be seen on the front of the beam. The buffers themselves are no longer present, but their fittings are still visible (Figure 1.22).

1.5 *Driving* Rocket

The driver and fireman stood on the 'footplate' behind *Rocket*'s firebox (Figure 1.23). When the locomotive and its train were ready to move, the driver would open the regulator valve. As the valve was opened further, more steam would pass from the boiler to the cylinders. Increasing the steam flow would increase *Rocket*'s speed of movement. The weight of the train, the gradient and the developing momentum would all determine the speed of travel up to its operating maximum of about 35 km/h (22 mph).

Figure 1.23 The simple iron 'footplate' was fitted to the rear of the frame. The buffing pads, drawbar bracket and reversing pedal are features of the footplate. (Michael R Bailey)

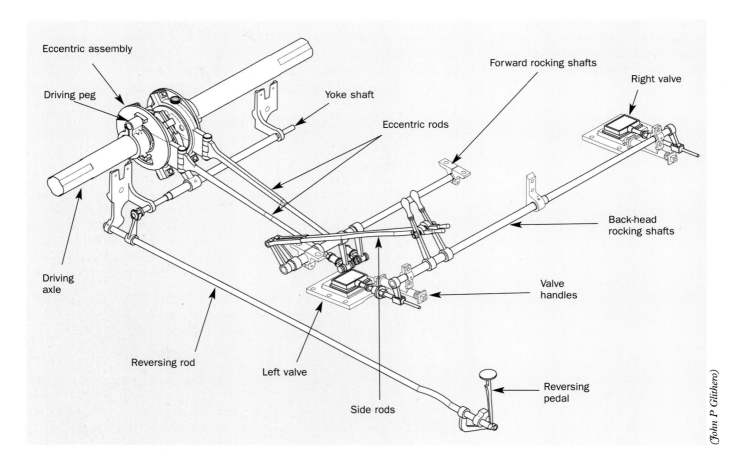

Eccentric assembly

Driving peg

Yoke shaft

Forward rocking shafts

Right valve

Eccentric rods

Back-head rocking shafts

Driving axle

Valve handles

Reversing rod

Left valve

Side rods

Reversing pedal

(John P Glithero)

Figure 1.24 To set Rocket's *direction of travel in forward or reverse, the driver engaged the eccentrics with either a forward or reverse peg fixed to the axle. He would depress a foot pedal, on the footplate, which shifted the eccentrics sideways from one peg to the other. The pegs engaged in slots in the sides of the eccentrics to drive them round when the axle rotated. Resetting the valves using the hand levers and engaging the alternative peg would cause the locomotive to set off in the opposite direction.*

There were no brakes on the locomotive. The driver slowed the train to a controlled halt by shutting the regulator valve to close off the steam supply. The resistances of all the moving components on the locomotive and the weight of its train would soon slow it down. Parking brakes on the tender and carriages would have held the train when stationary.

Rocket's ability to operate forwards or backwards depended on the reciprocating sequence of the steam valves above the cylinders (Figure 1.24). The two steam valves were driven by rods and rocking shafts from the driving axle. This motion resulted from the use of off-centre discs, or 'eccentrics', fitted around the axle, which rotated with it but whose off-centre action provided the reciprocating movement to the valve motion.

1.6 Rocket's water supply

The fireman stoked the fire with coke stored on the tender behind the locomotive. He also ensured that there was sufficient water in the boiler and in the firebox saddle. He kept himself aware of the water level by monitoring a glass 'sight gauge' fitted to the outside of the boiler (Figure 1.25). The fireman could also rely on 'try-cock' taps, set in the side of the boiler, which would emit steam or water when turned, to indicate the water level.

Brass pumps, bolted onto each side of the frame, pumped water into the boiler, from the reservoir on the tender (Figures 1.26 and 1.27). The pumps were driven by a pin on the back of each crosshead. Therefore, when Rocket had been stationary for

Figures 1.26 and 1.27 Detailed views of the rear of Rocket *showing the crosshead-driven boiler feed pumps and water pipes. (Science & Society Picture Library, National Railway Museum)*

any length of time, the driver had to drive it up and down the track for a time in order to pump water into the boiler.

The fireman watched the level of the water closely to ensure that it did not drop too low, which would have caused the firebox crown to overheat and distort. Similarly, too much water in the boiler would have caused some surplus to pass into the cylinders. This 'priming' of water would both have endangered the cylinders and significantly reduced *Rocket*'s efficiency.

The priming problem was addressed during *Rocket*'s first few months of operation. It was resolved by adding a dome on the top of the boiler, which provided a reservoir of 'dry' steam above the level of the turbulent water (Figures 1.28 and 1.29). A steam pipe with a vertical 'riser' inside the dome ensured that the dry steam was directed along the pipe to the regulator valve.

Rocket's brass 'dome', which has been a prominent feature in many illustrations and on the full-size replicas, had not been fitted at the time of the Rainhill Trials. The dome displaced the lock-up safety valve, which was then relocated to the rear of the boiler barrel. The successful fitting of the dome allowed the water level in the boiler to be raised by 75 mm, which ensured that the firebox crown was no longer at risk.

Figure 1.28 Detail of the top of Rocket's *boiler as built. Two safety valves are shown and no dome is present.*

Figure 1.29 Detail of the modified boiler top, showing the brass dome and the resited lock-up safety valve. (National Railway Museum)

2 *Rocket*'s place in locomotive development

Figure 2.1 William Hedley's Puffing Billy *of 1814, on display in the Science Museum, is the world's oldest surviving steam locomotive. Its single-flue boiler and parallel driving motion emphasise the major advancement in* Rocket's *boiler design and driving motion 15 years later. (Science & Society Picture Library)*

2.1 Early locomotives

Rocket was not the first steam locomotive. That honour goes back a further quarter of a century to the work of Richard Trevithick, the Cornish engineer who first demonstrated his experimental machines to sceptical industrialists. During the next 25 years, some of the country's most innovative engineers improved Trevithick's early work to produce machines of increasing power. These 'travelling engines' were useful to coal-mine owners, as they could move wagons of coal, at just 9 km/h (6 mph), to towns and ports more cheaply than by using horses.

The machines produced by the pioneer engineers – including Matthew Murray in Leeds, and the Northumberland engineers William Hedley from Wylam (Figure 2.1) and George Stephenson from Killingworth – helped to reduce the price of coal delivered to the markets. The Stockton & Darlington Railway was opened in 1825 to transport coal from the coalfields of West Durham to the shipping staithes on the River Tees. It was built by George Stephenson and was the first public railway to use locomotive haulage. His several locomotives included *Locomotion*, which is now preserved in Darlington.

Locomotion and its fellow travelling engines worked well at first, and attracted a lot of attention to the benefits of using them. However, their components were vulnerable to breakage from the rigours of everyday use, and they spent a lot of time under repair. This was made worse by the condition of the early railway track, which deteriorated rapidly with use. If railways were to develop into major arteries between urban centres, significant improvements in design, materials and methods of manufacture would be required.

2.2 Development

The Liverpool & Manchester Railway was the first main-line railway, linking the fast-developing port city of Liverpool with the equally fast-developing manufacturing city of Manchester. It was built to carry two-way traffic, especially foodstuffs, raw materials, such as cotton and coal, and manufactured goods, such as cotton fabrics and machinery. It also introduced a passenger service between the cities, the popularity of which was quite unexpected.

This new 'main-line' mode of transport required a new type of motive power. George Stephenson was the railway's Chief Engineer and, while the line was being built, he argued strongly that improved steam locomotives should be adopted. However, there remained doubts in the minds of some of the company's directors. The slow speed, low power and unreliability of engines, such as *Locomotion*, would have to be much improved for use with this demanding new service.

In 1828, George Stephenson was fully preoccupied supervising the building of the railway. It was therefore left to Robert Stephenson, then just 24 years old, to begin a major development programme to improve the locomotive. In conjunction with a team of able craftsmen at his Newcastle factory, Robert considered each component carefully. The team sought to try out improvements that would be more robust and economic for main-line operation, through better design, materials and manufacturing methods. Robert also recruited a draughtsman, who prepared drawings to arrange all the components in the best way to meet the severe space and weight limitations.

Each improvement was made and fitted onto several experimental locomotives. These were sold to customers in Britain, France and America, where each was tried out, prompting ideas for further improvements. Over the next three years an extraordinary number of improvements were made to locomotive technology. It was almost comparable to today's rapid development of computer and mobile-phone technology, as each of Stephenson's innovations superseded previous improvements. The cumbersome and unreliable colliery 'travelling engine' was transformed into a more robust, reliable and economic locomotive, suitable for main-line operation. *Rocket* was one of the prototypes, and a most important example of this development effort.

Several trials were carried out, with different types of boiler, in attempts to generate a greater volume of steam. *Locomotion* and other early locomotives had one large flue inside the boiler. It contained the fire at one end and the hot gases were sent up the chimney at the other. Others, such as *Lancashire Witch*, were fitted with two large flues in an attempt to increase the heating surface and thereby increase steam production.

Rocket's multitubular boiler, with its much greater heating surface, was therefore a major improvement – adopted for all subsequent locomotives. The idea of increasing the heating surface by using a cluster of small tubes, rather than just one or two flue tubes, came from Henry Booth, the energetic Secretary of the Liverpool & Manchester Railway. It was, however, left to Robert Stephenson and his capable assistants to work out the boiler and firebox configuration that would allow this idea to be put into effect. The two Stephensons discussed the form for a separate firebox, and sketched out what would be required. A firm of Liverpool coppersmiths, more used to fitting protective copper sheets to the bottoms of ships, was employed to make the firebox 'saddle'. They used copper plates specially formed by hand and riveted together. The saddle was then sent to Newcastle to be fitted to the locomotive.

The introduction of steel leaf springs was a major innovation during the development period (Figure 2.2). Unlike the earlier colliery engines, which only had primitive forms of suspension, the new engines were much more stable. The number of breakages, both on the locomotives and with the track, was much reduced. The springs also allowed the use of the more direct, and much simpler, crosshead and connecting rod to transmit the power of the steam to the wheels. *Rocket* was built with both steel springs and direct transmission, taking full advantage of the new experience that had been gained.

Even though Robert Stephenson's development programme had been so successful, some railway directors continued to express grave doubts about complete reliance on locomotives. From the experience on the Stockton & Darlington line, they continued to fear that they would be unreliable and costly to maintain. In spite of this opposition, George Stephenson campaigned vigorously for using locomotives, and his arguments led to the setting up of the Rainhill Trials of October 1829.

2.3 Further improvements

From the experience gained both during and after the Rainhill Trials, further improvements were made and *Rocket*'s design quickly became superseded. The first problem to be resolved was the pitching and rolling action at speed brought about by the piston thrusts and the resulting spring deflection. The next locomotives to be built in Newcastle had their cylinders fitted in a near-horizontal position, which considerably reduced this deflection and improved stability.

The next important innovation was the fitting of a dome on top of the boiler. The steam inside the dome was 'drier' than that in the top of the boiler generally,

Figure 2.2 The Lancashire Witch *of July 1828 was one of the first examples of Robert Stephenson's development programme. It was fitted with steel leaf springs and direct drive from piston to wheel using a crosshead and slide bars. Its boiler contained two fire flues. After its successful operation on the Bolton & Leigh Railway in Lancashire, the direct drive arrangement was adopted for* Rocket. *(Science Museum)*

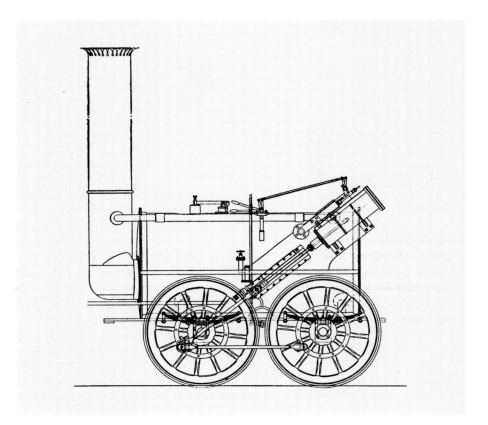

Figure 2.3 Contemporary view of Invicta, *showing its steam manifold above the boiler. The benefits of obtaining drier steam through the manifold led directly to steam domes being used on the subsequent locomotives. (Science & Society Picture Library)*

being less affected by the turbulence of the water. The dome was thus a simple solution to the problem of water being carried into the cylinders, which significantly reduced the efficiency of *Rocket* and other early locomotives. The use of a steam manifold above the boiler was first tried out on another early Stephenson locomotive, *Invicta* (Figure 2.3), on the Canterbury & Whitstable Railway. This historic locomotive is also preserved, in Canterbury.

The fitting of *Rocket*'s chimney directly to its front tube plate was unsatisfactory. There was little room for the pipes that turned the exhaust steam up into the base of the chimney, which restricted the passage of the hot gases from the small tubes to the atmosphere. The introduction of a larger 'smokebox', as an efficient vacuum chamber, improved both the locomotive's combustion and steam-raising capabilities.

Further improvements were incorporated into the later prototype locomotives during the rapid developments of 1830 (Figure 2.4). The firebox was redesigned to form a complete copper box, which was fitted inside an extension of the main boiler barrel. This allowed water to circulate freely between them, without the need for external pipes such as those fitted to *Rocket*.

The last, and perhaps biggest, improvement was the relocation of the cylinders to the front end of the locomotive. They were placed between the wheels and under the smokebox to prevent the loss of some of the heat from the steam before it could work in the cylinders. This more efficient use of the steam reduced the amount, and cost, of the coke that was burnt. It meant, however, that this 'inside' driving motion required a cranked axle to effect the drive. Although this form of axle was more expensive to make, both driving motions were brought closer together to provide a more stable ride at speed than on the 'outside'-cylinder locomotives.

All the innovations were brought together in the *Planet* class of engines (Figure 2.5). The first was completed in September 1830. This was the world's first main-line locomotive type, adopted on several of the earliest railways in Britain, Europe and North America.

Figure 2.4 The locomotives Northumbrian *and* Majestic *were built at the Stephensons' factory in the summer of 1830. They were the first to be fitted with both smokeboxes and fireboxes integrated with the boiler. (Science Museum)*

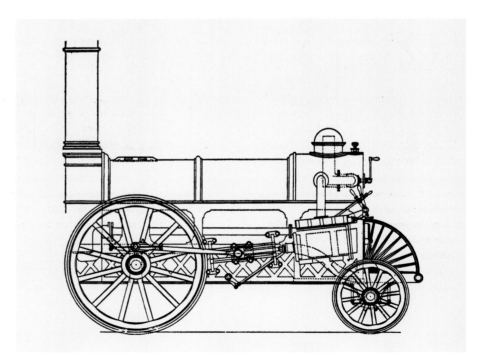

Figure 2.5 The Planet class of locomotives was the culmination of Robert Stephenson's development programme. A working replica of Planet is part of the collections of the Museum of Science & Industry in Manchester. (Photo courtesy of the Museum of Science & Industry in Manchester)

In less than three years of development work, Robert Stephenson had transformed locomotive design from the cumbersome colliery types of the Stockton & Darlington Railway to the main-line Planet class, from which all later designs were derived.

3 The Rainhill Trials

Figure 3.1 *'Stipulations and Conditions' of the Rainhill Trials, as preserved in the notebook of John Urpeth Rastrick. The notebook itself is now in the collections of the Science Museum (Inv. No. 1945-108). (Science & Society Picture Library)*

3.1 'Stipulations and Conditions'

The idea to hold the Rainhill competition came in the spring of 1829, as a means to resolve the worries of the Liverpool & Manchester Railway directors. Because they were risking so much of their money on the whole railway venture, it was important

Figure 3.2 A contemporary illustration of Rocket *as built, showing its angled cylinders, boiler-top safety valves and firebox water and steam pipes.*

for them to determine what was the best form of motive power to use. Should they invest in track-side steam engines and winding ropes, or adopt steam locomotives as George Stephenson so strongly recommended? If they were to select locomotives, should they be built at the Stephenson factory, as he also strongly recommended, or by other manufacturers? A massive prize of £500 was to be awarded to the engineer who could design and build a locomotive suitable for main-line operations.

The performance trials were the opportunity for the Stephensons to demonstrate, in competition with other contenders, that their locomotives were, indeed, the best available for main-line service. The call for entries to the trials coincided with their development programme, and Robert Stephenson accordingly adapted the developing designs to meet the laid-down requirements for the trials (Figure 3.1).

Figure 3.3 Rocket, Sans Pareil *and* Novelty *were the main contenders for the £500 premium prize at the Rainhill Trials. Only* Rocket *completed the full trial programme successfully, and it was the convincing winner. (Science & Society Picture Library)*

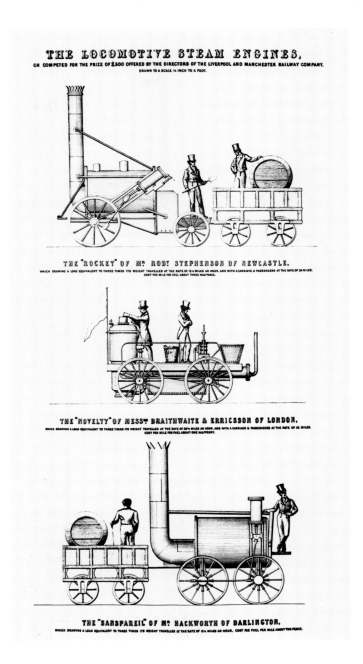

THE LOCOMOTIVE STEAM ENGINES,

WHICH COMPETED FOR THE PRIZE OF £500 OFFERED BY THE DIRECTORS OF THE LIVERPOOL AND MANCHESTER RAILWAY COMPANY.

DRAWN TO A SCALE ¼ INCH TO A FOOT.

THE "ROCKET" OF MR. ROBT. STEPHENSON OF NEWCASTLE,

WHICH DRAWING A LOAD EQUIVALENT TO THREE TIMES ITS WEIGHT TRAVELLED AT THE RATE OF 12½ MILES AN HOUR, AND WITH A CARRIAGE & PASSENGERS AT THE RATE OF 24 MILES. COST PER MILE FOR FUEL ABOUT THREE HALFPENCE.

THE "NOVELTY" OF MESSR. BRAITHWAITE & ERRICSSON OF LONDON,

WHICH DRAWING A LOAD EQUIVALENT TO THREE TIMES ITS WEIGHT TRAVELLED AT THE RATE OF 20½ MILES AN HOUR, AND WITH A CARRIAGE & PASSENGERS AT THE RATE OF 32 MILES. COST PER MILE FOR FUEL ABOUT ONE HALFPENNY.

THE "SANSPAREIL" OF MR. HACKWORTH OF DARLINGTON,

WHICH DRAWING A LOAD EQUIVALENT TO THREE TIMES ITS WEIGHT TRAVELLED AT THE RATE OF 15½ MILES AN HOUR. COST FOR FUEL PER MILE ABOUT TWO PENCE.

The requirements called for lightweight but powerful locomotives that were capable of drawing three times their own weight at 10 mph (16 km/h) or more. The entries could be either six-wheeled engines of no more than 6 tons, or four-wheeled engines of no more than 4½ tons. All four of the engines that were entered, including *Rocket* (Figure 3.2), were four-wheeled machines with this limiting weight restriction.

Henry Booth and George Stephenson entered *Rocket* for the competition, and Robert Stephenson also put his name to the entry during its construction. The other contenders (Figure 3.3) were *Novelty* built by John Braithwaite and John Ericsson in London, *Sans Pareil* built by Timothy Hackworth in Shildon, County Durham, and *Perseverance* built by Timothy Burstall in Edinburgh. A fifth contender, *Cycloped*, built to the design of Thomas Brandreth, was a strange vehicle driven by two horses on a treadmill. In the event, only *Rocket*, *Novelty* and *Sans Pareil* were serious contenders.

As soon as it had been completed in September 1829, Robert Stephenson tried *Rocket* out on the Killingworth wagonway, north of Newcastle, to make sure it worked well, and to make any adjustments that were necessary. It achieved its design speed of 12 mph (19 km/h) quite easily, and required only minor adjustments back at the factory. It was soon packed up and despatched by road via Carlisle, where it was placed aboard a ship bound for Liverpool. On arrival, it was found that the small carrying wheels underneath the footplate did not fit. Stephenson's men quickly found another wheel set on a wagon and, although they were slightly oversize, fitted them to *Rocket*. With this set, the locomotive took part in the trials.

Rocket was painted yellow, as were the new first-class carriages being built for service on the line. The choice of yellow was deliberate, as it was the colour used for high-speed stage coaches, then the main form of long-distance road conveyance. Yellow would therefore symbolise speed in the minds of the travelling public. This demonstrated an early form of corporate identity, and awareness of perception and association. The chimney was painted white, probably to emphasise the cleanliness from the use of coke at a time when people were concerned about the environment (Figure 3.4).

3.2 The trials

The trials (Figures 3.5 and 3.6) took place at Rainhill, a small village some 15 kilometres east of Liverpool. It had a 3-kilometre (1¾-mile) length of level track that was ideal for the purposes. There was considerable interest from the public, who flocked in large numbers to witness the event, and a grandstand had to be built to accommodate them. Three independent judges, John Rastrick, Nicholas Wood and John Kennedy, all experienced and well-known mechanical engineers, set down the specific requirements for the trials, and adjudicated over the performance of the locomotives.

Figure 3.4 Replica of Rocket *in steam at the National Railway Museum in York, showing its form and livery as it appeared at the Rainhill Trials. The recent study into the locomotive's history reveals that some details on the replica are different from those of the original form. (Science & Society Picture Library)*

The first trial took place on the morning of 8 October. It was composed of ten timed round trips along the Rainhill level, which represented 5 miles (8 kilometres) of acceleration and deceleration and 30 miles (48 kilometres) at an operating speed, chosen to represent a journey between Liverpool (Edge Hill) and Manchester. *Rocket* hauled two carriages loaded with stones to a gross weight, including its tender, of 12¾ tons, calculated to be three times that of the locomotive itself. The trial took 3 hours, 11 minutes and 48 seconds to complete. During this time, the crew became more adept and confident at driving and firing, and trip speeds gradually rose from 12.7 to 14.54 mph (19.9 to 23.3 km/h), with the last trip being made at 19.15 mph (30.6 km/h) (Figure 3.7).

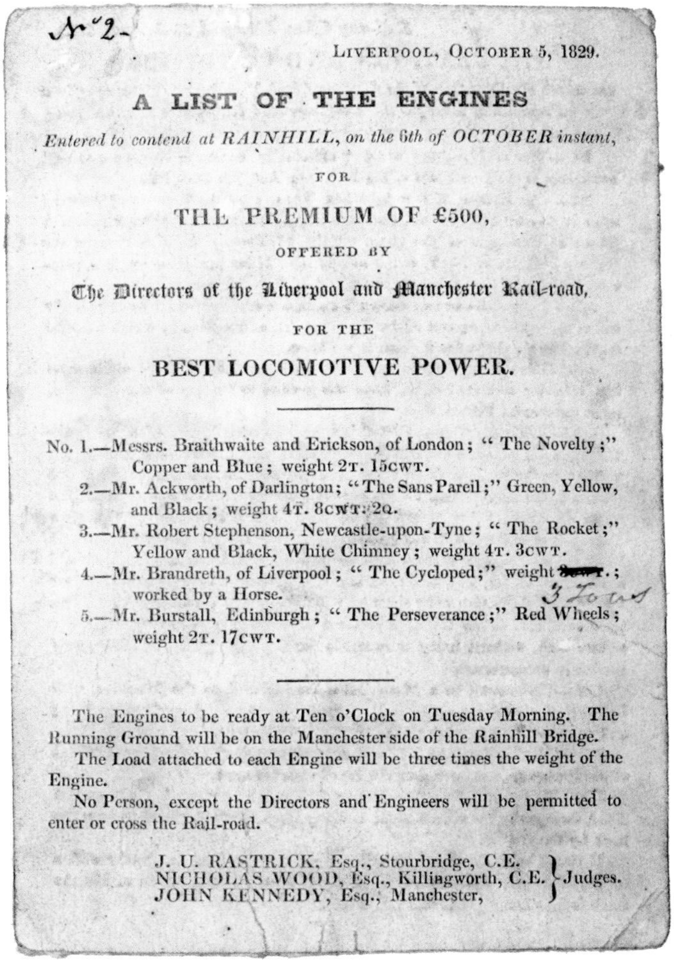

No. 2

LIVERPOOL, OCTOBER 5, 1829.

A LIST OF THE ENGINES

Entered to contend at RAINHILL, on the 6th of OCTOBER instant,

FOR

THE PREMIUM OF £500,

OFFERED BY

𝕿𝖍𝖊 𝕯𝖎𝖗𝖊𝖈𝖙𝖔𝖗𝖘 𝖔𝖋 𝖙𝖍𝖊 𝕷𝖎𝖛𝖊𝖗𝖕𝖔𝖔𝖑 𝖆𝖓𝖉 𝕸𝖆𝖓𝖈𝖍𝖊𝖘𝖙𝖊𝖗 𝕽𝖆𝖎𝖑-𝖗𝖔𝖆𝖉,

FOR THE

BEST LOCOMOTIVE POWER.

No. 1.—Messrs. Braithwaite and Erickson, of London; " The Novelty;" Copper and Blue; weight 2T. 15CWT.

2.—Mr. Ackworth, of Darlington; "The Sans Pareil;" Green, Yellow, and Black; weight 4T. 8CWT. 2Q.

3.—Mr. Robert Stephenson, Newcastle-upon-Tyne; " The Rocket;" Yellow and Black, White Chimney; weight 4T. 3CWT.

4.—Mr. Brandreth, of Liverpool; " The Cycloped;" weight ~~3T.~~; 3 Tons worked by a Horse.

5.—Mr. Burstall, Edinburgh; " The Perseverance;" Red Wheels; weight 2T. 17CWT.

The Engines to be ready at Ten o'Clock on Tuesday Morning. The Running Ground will be on the Manchester side of the Rainhill Bridge.

The Load attached to each Engine will be three times the weight of the Engine.

No Person, except the Directors and Engineers will be permitted to enter or cross the Rail-road.

J. U. RASTRICK, Esq., Stourbridge, C.E.
NICHOLAS WOOD, Esq., Killingworth, C.E. } Judges.
JOHN KENNEDY, Esq., Manchester,

Figure 3.5 A list of the engines entered for the Rainhill Trials, recorded in Rastrick's notebook. (Science & Society Picture Library)

The second trial followed after a pause of just 15 minutes, which was long enough to take on fresh supplies of water and coke. It was similar to the first trial and represented the return trip from Manchester back to Liverpool. This time, with the crew now well used to getting the best out of *Rocket*, the average trip speeds rose from 13.06 to 15.06 mph (20.9 to 24.1 km/h), and again ended with a flourish on the last run, of 24.11 mph (38.6 km/h).

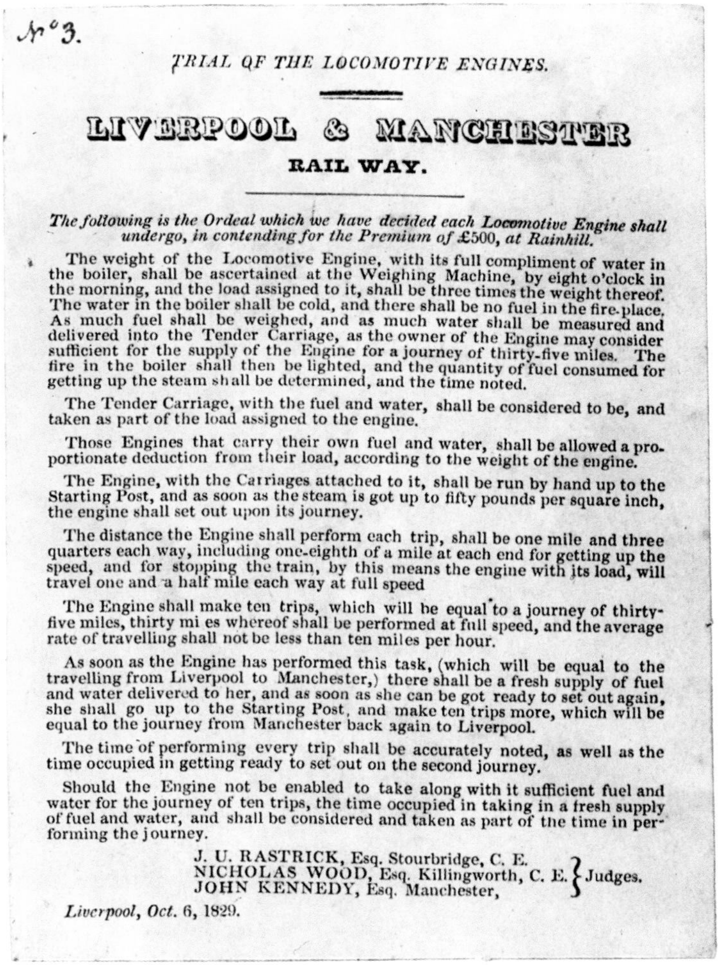

Figure 3.6 The requirements of the Rainhill Trials, recorded in Rastrick's notebook. (Science & Society PIcture Library)

The content of Figure 3.6:

No. 3.

TRIAL OF THE LOCOMOTIVE ENGINES.

LIVERPOOL & MANCHESTER
RAIL WAY.

The following is the Ordeal which we have decided each Locomotive Engine shall undergo, in contending for the Premium of £500, at Rainhill.

The weight of the Locomotive Engine, with its full compliment of water in the boiler, shall be ascertained at the Weighing Machine, by eight o'clock in the morning, and the load assigned to it, shall be three times the weight thereof. The water in the boiler shall be cold, and there shall be no fuel in the fire-place. As much fuel shall be weighed, and as much water shall be measured and delivered into the Tender Carriage, as the owner of the Engine may consider sufficient for the supply of the Engine for a journey of thirty-five miles. The fire in the boiler shall then be lighted, and the quantity of fuel consumed for getting up the steam shall be determined, and the time noted.

The Tender Carriage, with the fuel and water, shall be considered to be, and taken as part of the load assigned to the engine.

Those Engines that carry their own fuel and water, shall be allowed a proportionate deduction from their load, according to the weight of the engine.

The Engine, with the Carriages attached to it, shall be run by hand up to the Starting Post, and as soon as the steam is got up to fifty pounds per square inch, the engine shall set out upon its journey.

The distance the Engine shall perform each trip, shall be one mile and three quarters each way, including one-eighth of a mile at each end for getting up the speed, and for stopping the train, by this means the engine with its load, will travel one and a half mile each way at full speed

The Engine shall make ten trips, which will be equal to a journey of thirty-five miles, thirty mi es whereof shall be performed at full speed, and the average rate of travelling shall not be less than ten miles per hour.

As soon as the Engine has performed this task, (which will be equal to the travelling from Liverpool to Manchester,) there shall be a fresh supply of fuel and water delivered to her, and as soon as she can be got ready to set out again, she shall go up to the Starting Post, and make ten trips more, which will be equal to the journey from Manchester back again to Liverpool.

The time of performing every trip shall be accurately noted, as well as the time occupied in getting ready to set out on the second journey.

Should the Engine not be enabled to take along with it sufficient fuel and water for the journey of ten trips, the time occupied in taking in a fresh supply of fuel and water, and shall be considered and taken as part of the time in performing the journey.

J. U. RASTRICK, Esq. Stourbridge, C. E. }
NICHOLAS WOOD, Esq. Killingworth, C. E. } Judges.
JOHN KENNEDY, Esq. Manchester, }

Liverpool, Oct. 6, 1829.

The other contenders were tried over the next two days. *Perseverance* and *Cycloped* were unable to meet the trial requirements, however, and were withdrawn. Although *Novelty* was the crowd's favourite and performed well when first being demonstrated, component failures during its trial runs forced Braithwaite and Ericsson to withdraw it from the competition. *Sans Pareil* was therefore the leading competitor to *Rocket*. It did well to begin with, but problems with a pump and a cylinder meant that it, too, failed to complete the trials, leaving *Rocket* as the runaway victor.

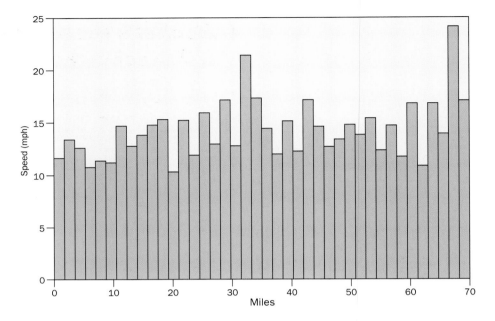

Figure 3.7 The speed achieved by Rocket *on each of its individual trips made during the trial on 8 October 1829. The accumulated distance of 70 miles (112 kilometres) actually exceeded, by 10 miles (16 kilometres), the distance from Liverpool (Edge Hill) to Manchester and back.*

As if to celebrate and reinforce its success, George Stephenson arranged for *Rocket* to make two trips along the Rainhill level on its own, in front of the crowds. It achieved a speed of no less than 35 mph (56 km/h), or three times its design speed. This was a world speed record. It also demonstrated to the assembled crowd that steam locomotives could transport people at sustained speeds greater than could be achieved with horses. The crowd understood well that what they were witnessing was the beginning of a new transport era, with enormous potential for mobility and economic benefits.

The two Stephensons and Henry Booth duly received the £500 premium from the directors of the Liverpool & Manchester Railway. From that moment, locomotives were confirmed as the motive power to be adopted by the railway, and all main-line railways thereafter. Robert Stephenson continued his development efforts, and introduced several further innovations that led to the *Planet* locomotive class being adopted for the railway's early operation.

4 *Rocket*'s service on the Liverpool & Manchester Railway

Figure 4.1 Rocket *being admired by the public at Edge Hill, Liverpool. (Science & Society Picture Library)*

4.1 Completion and opening

After the Rainhill Trials *Rocket* was bought by the railway company for use on the line. It had become famous, however, and many people wanted to see it and ride behind it (Figure 4.1). For several weeks the directors allowed influential people to travel on trains between Liverpool and Rainhill to experience rail travel at speed (Figure 4.2). It also built up confidence in the railway itself, as reflected in the company's buoyant share price. Thomas Creevey, a Liverpool Member of Parliament, was one such traveller, but he was very nervous about *Rocket*'s pitching and swaying at speed:

> the quickest motion is to me frightful: it is really flying, and it is impossible to divest yourself of the notion of instant death to all upon the least accident happening.

Figure 4.2 Contemporary sketch of Rocket *hauling passenger vehicles and passing through Olive Mount cutting, Liverpool. (Science & Society Picture Library)*

Figure 4.3 The scene at Edge Hill, Liverpool on the morning of the opening of the Liverpool & Manchester Railway, 15 September 1830. The 'Moorish Arch', through which all the special trains passed, symbolised a gateway to a new era. Rocket *hauled one of the special trains on this important occasion. (Science & Society Picture Library)*

Once the initial enthusiasm had died down, however, *Rocket* was put to more menial work. It was required to draw wagons of rock, earth and other material to places along the route where the railway was still being built. This was particularly the case for building up the embankment across the boggy Chat Moss near Salford. Although it drew the first train, conveying the directors, across the Moss on 28 December 1829, it continued to be used for several months afterwards, helping to consolidate the unstable embankment.

Just before the railway was opened for public service, the company ran several special trains with invited guests to publicise the event. One of the passengers was Frances (Fanny) Kemble, a young actress who was appearing in a Liverpool play. George Stephenson himself escorted her, and she later described her experience with a youthful enthusiasm, which contrasted with Creevey's concerns:

> We were introduced to the little engine which was to drag us along the rails. She (for they make these curious little fire horses all mares) consisted of a boiler, a stove, a platform, a bench, and behind the bench a barrel containing enough water to prevent her being thirsty for fifteen miles …. This snorting little animal, which I felt rather

Figure 4.4 The memorial to William Huskisson at Parkside, midway between Liverpool and Manchester. It marks the spot where Rocket *fatally wounded the Liverpool MP on the railway's opening day. (Railtrack)*

inclined to pat, was then harnessed to our carriage, and Mr. Stephenson, having taken me on the bench of the engine with him ... the engine ... was set off at its utmost speed, 35 miles an hour, swifter than a bird flies .... You cannot conceive what that sensation of cutting the air was; the motion is as smooth as possible, too .... I stood up, and with my bonnet off 'drank the air before me' .... When I closed my eyes this sensation of flying was quite delightful.

The Liverpool & Manchester Railway was ceremonially opened on 15 September 1830 (Figure 4.3). Many dignitaries attended, including the prime minister, the Duke of Wellington. It was a day of great significance that marked the beginning of a new era. All the special trains passed through a large 'Moorish Arch' at Edge Hill, Liverpool, and the crowds turned out in their thousands all along the route.

The day was marked by tragedy, however, when *Rocket* was involved in an accident. It ran over and fatally wounded the Liverpool MP, and former government minister, William Huskisson. The several special trains conveying the guests had stopped at Parkside, halfway from Liverpool to Manchester, to replenish their water tanks. Contrary to the advice they were given, several people, including Huskisson, who was partially lame, got down onto the track. As *Rocket* approached with its train on the adjacent track, a warning was shouted, but he was unable to move quickly

Figure 4.5 *Embankment across Chat Moss to the west of Manchester, on which* Rocket *was employed for several months hauling train loads of rock and other materials which were used to help make the embankment more stable. (Science & Society Picture Library)*

enough, and was knocked over. He was carried up onto the footplate of *Rocket*, which then ran towards Manchester at top speed to get him to a surgeon, but he later died from loss of blood and shock.

The incident has been remembered ever since by a memorial to Huskisson placed by the side of the track at Parkside (Figure 4.4). Travellers between Liverpool and Manchester daily pass the site, where the memorial records both the sad occasion of the incident and the importance of the railway's opening:

> the accident ... which changed a moment of the noblest exultation and triumph that science and genius had ever achieved into one of desolation and mourning ....

4.2 Operation, accidents and modifications

By the time of the railway's opening, *Rocket*'s design was already outdated. The later Stephenson locomotives significantly reduced the cost of operating trains, and were used on the popular passenger workings. *Rocket* continued to be used on works trains from Salford, taking spoil to Chat Moss, where efforts continued to make the embankment more stable (Figure 4.5).

53

Only five weeks after the opening of the line, *Rocket* was involved in another of the serious accidents that marred its career. In spite of a directive that unauthorised persons should not travel on the engines, a railway enthusiast, Henry Hunter, had been allowed to ride on the tender as a works train was being propelled back to Salford. One of the tender axles broke and derailed the train, the jerk projecting Hunter under the wheels of the tender and locomotive. He was afterwards 'found to be quite dead'.

Rocket and its tender were damaged and taken back to Liverpool for repairs. While the locomotive was being fixed, the company decided to rebuild it to incorporate some of the improvements that had been successfully adopted on the later locomotives. They called in a firm of Liverpool contractors to undertake the work. It was on this occasion that the opportunity was taken to fit the steam dome and internal steam pipe. In addition, the second safety valve was relocated, and a smokebox, ashbox and shorter chimney put on. The contractors also fitted the existing water-filled firebox back plate, together with new water feed pipes and a raised fire grate.

In its much-improved condition, *Rocket* was used as a passenger locomotive for a few weeks from the end of 1830. This was a big help to the railway, which was then short of locomotives as it struggled to keep up with the extraordinarily high demand for passenger travel. It was on just such a working in January 1831 that *Rocket* suffered the worst accident of its short career. It derailed in Olive Mount cutting near Liverpool, fell over on its side and was significantly damaged, thankfully without loss of life (Figure 4.6).

It was returned to Edge Hill, where contractors again carried out repairs. This time it was decided to lower the cylinders from their angled fitting to a near-horizontal alignment. This involved making and fitting the large, rear-mounted cylinder-carrying frames that remain on the locomotive to this day. The contractors exchanged the cylinders, side for side, and inverted them, before fitting them to the new frames. They made repairs to the damaged front end, and built on a buffer beam. The surviving wooden driving wheels probably date from this rebuild.

Rocket probably returned to passenger service after this rebuild. However, by the autumn of 1831, the railway had enough *Planet*-class locomotives for its services, and *Rocket* was relegated to being a works engine again. In September 1832, an independent branch railway from Wigan to the Manchester line was opened. *Rocket* was loaned to the Wigan Branch Railway for the first few weeks of the new service. It was during its time on this line that it was involved in yet another accident, this time a collision with a *Planet*-type engine pulling a coal train. *Rocket* sustained damage that cost £74 14s 7d (£74.73p) to repair. This work was carried out in the new Edge Hill workshops, and completed in January 1833.

Several minor improvements were made on this occasion. The cylinders were rebored, and improved pistons were fitted, incorporating better steam-tight brass

Figure 4.6 Rocket, *as first modified, hauling a passenger train through Olive Mount cutting, Liverpool. It suffered its worst derailment and damage here, following which substantial repairs and modifications were carried out. (Science & Society Picture Library)*

piston rings. It is possible that one of the driving wheels was remade on this occasion, following the accident damage. In 1833, however, newer and larger locomotives were being introduced onto the railway, and it was apparent that *Rocket* could no longer justify further expenditure to keep it in service. From that year, it was probably only used for stand-by duties and occasional works trains.

4.3 Experimental use

The early 1830s was a period of intense interest in steam engine development. A number of inventors sought to promote their ideas, and contacted the railway's directors asking to try them out on its locomotives. *Rocket*'s availability meant that it was used as a test-bed for some of these trials.

It was first used as a vehicle to carry out experiments on behalf of a freelance engineer, Richard Badnall. He promoted the idea of improving railway alignments by grading them to take advantage of gravity for acceleration and deceleration. This would be in accordance with prevailing loads and stopping places, using a form of pendulum motion. His 'undulating railways' would continue to use steam locomotives, but he argued that their economy would be significantly enhanced by favourable gradients.

Rocket was used as a trial vehicle to test the momentum characteristics under different gradients, speeds and loads. It was soon withdrawn, however, as it became 'so much out of order'. After the directors' initial enthusiasm, it became apparent that the predicted cost savings were not going to be fulfilled, and the project was abandoned.

In October 1834, *Rocket* was used for another trial, this time of a revolutionary new 'rotary engine'. Its inventor was Lord Dundonald, a rear admiral in the Royal Navy. He was famous as a war hero, but he also liked to pursue ideas for new technology. He developed his rotary steam engine principally for application to ships, but he was anxious to demonstrate its application to railway locomotives (Figure 4.7).

A prototype twin-cylindered rotary engine was fitted around *Rocket*'s driving axle and anchored to its frame. Within the engine housings, driving vanes were clamped to the axles. They were driven by steam pressure, and revolved within the housings to rotate the axle. For these trials, the normal cylinders and motion were disconnected and reliance placed on the rotary engine. The engine was a big failure, however, probably because of the inability of its seals to retain steam pressure. Although further trials were made on other locomotives near London, the engines were never a practicable proposition for railway application.

Figure 4.7 Lord Dundonald's twin-cylindered rotary engine adapted to locomotive propulsion. This configuration was similar to that adopted for Rocket*'s driving axle. (The Earl of Dundonald; National Archives of Scotland, ref. GD233/1/2/3)*

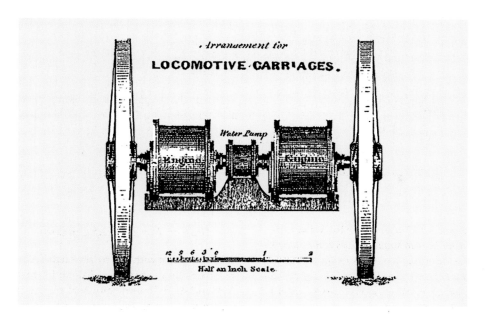

5 *Rocket* after 1836: colliery workhorse and museum exhibit

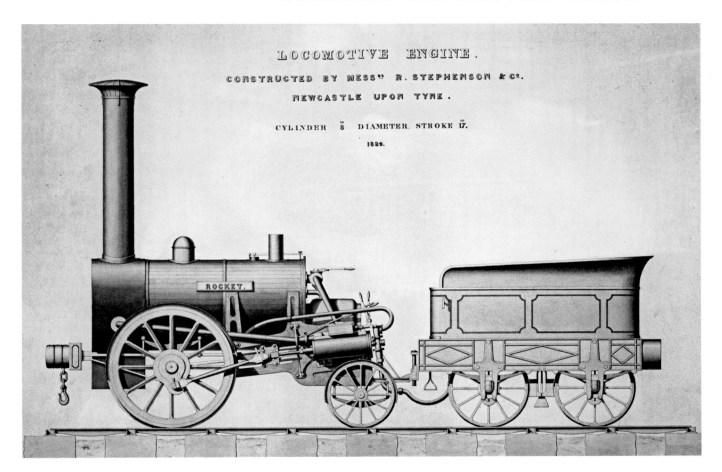

LOCOMOTIVE ENGINE.

CONSTRUCTED BY MESS.ʳˢ R. STEPHENSON & Cᵒ.

NEWCASTLE UPON TYNE.

CYLINDER 8 DIAMETER. STROKE 17.

1829.

ROCKET.

Figure 5.1 This drawing of Rocket *was prepared in 1836 for the directors of the Liverpool & Manchester Railway, before its sale to the Earl of Carlisle. It shows the extent of the locomotive's rebuilding during its service with the railway. (Science & Society Picture Library)*

5.1 Sale to the Earl of Carlisle

After the trials with the rotary engine, *Rocket* was laid aside, out of use, at the Edge Hill workshops. It remained there for many months until, in June 1836, the Liverpool & Manchester Railway directors offered it for sale on the second-hand market. Before selling it, however, they arranged for a drawing to be made of the locomotive and

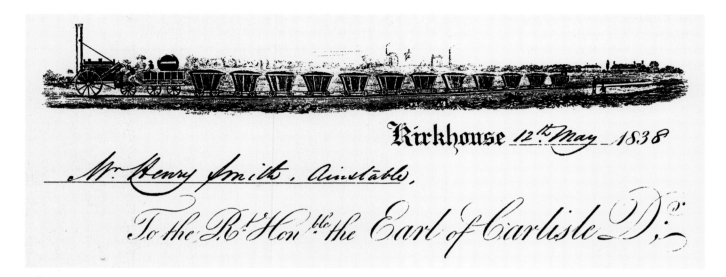

Figure 5.2 Rocket-and-train vignette from the Earl of Carlisle's stationery. (C Attenborough)

tender (Figure 5.1). This was probably out of sentiment, as it had no practical value to them. The drawing, which is now in the Science Museum in London, illustrates what *Rocket* looked like after the several rebuildings, and in the form in which it was sold.

In October 1836, the Earl of Carlisle bought the locomotive for £300 (Figure 5.2). This was on the recommendation of his innovative colliery agent, James Thompson. The Earl's standard-gauge railway system served his colliery network in the Naworth coalfield of Cumberland. This network was linked to the new Newcastle & Carlisle Railway, along which the coal was to be forwarded to the markets and shipping points. The line had just been converted and extended from a horse-operated system, and it was important for Thompson to acquire a locomotive with a light axle load to run over the colliery system's lightweight rails. *Rocket* fulfilled this requirement.

The locomotive was based at the colliery workshops in the small village of Kirkhouse, where some further repairs and modifications were made before it entered service. Extensions were bolted underneath its front buffer beam to enable it to work with the small coal-carrying chaldron wagons (Figure 5.3). These had lower buffer heights than the main-line vehicles that *Rocket* had previously pulled. It began service, pulling coal wagons, in March 1837.

5.2 The Alston election run

In August 1837, the flamboyant James Thompson and his brother, Mark, used *Rocket* in an extraordinary demonstration of the capabilities of 'modern' transport.

Figure 5.3 Rocket's buffer beam showing the supplementary buffers for working with chaldron wagons on the Naworth colliery railway. (Science & Society Picture Library)

Following Queen Victoria's accession to the throne that year, there was a general election, held on 7 and 8 August. After the close of the polls for the East Cumberland constituency in the market town of Alston, the voting returns were conveyed to the Returning Officer in Carlisle, 48 kilometres away, in just 62 minutes.

The exact circumstances by which this was achieved were not recorded, but it is presumed that a Deputy Returning Officer participated in this high-speed endeavour and accompanied the returns throughout the journey. He would have travelled on horseback from Alston town centre along the Carlisle turnpike road (the present-day A689) for 16 kilometres. This gallop over the undulating road would probably have been achieved using three separate horses, the relief horses waiting by the roadside. It is estimated that an average speed of 35 km/h (22 mph) could have been achieved, and the journey completed in 27 minutes.

Rocket was standing ready where the turnpike crossed the Naworth colliery railway, and the officer would have quickly transferred to its footplate. With Mark Thompson as the driver, the locomotive accelerated quickly and probably ran at 56 km/h (35 mph) for the 8-kilometre run to Kirkhouse, where it ran down a steep incline to the workshop level. Here, the officer transferred to a main-line locomotive of the Newcastle & Carlisle Railway for the dash to Carlisle station, and a short ride on horseback to the Returning Officer waiting in the city centre. It is possible that a journey of just one hour was being attempted, but even 62 minutes was a remarkable achievement for the day.

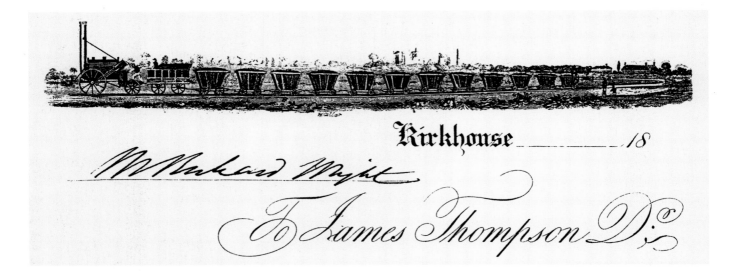

Figure 5.4 Rocket-*and-train vignette from James Thompson's stationery. (C Attenborough)*

5.3 *End of service and storage*

From 1838, the Earl of Carlisle leased the whole colliery system to James Thompson (Figure 5.4). In taking over all the equipment, Thompson also acquired *Rocket*, and continued to use it to haul trains of coal wagons to Kirkhouse for about two years. During this time, however, it seems to have had yet another collision, this time with some chaldron wagons. Some of its leading framework was broken and its buffer beam bent downwards. This distortion of the buffer beam can still be seen on the locomotive. It was withdrawn from service in about 1840, probably because it had become too expensive to maintain (Figure 5.5).

Thompson could not bring himself to scrap *Rocket*, however, no doubt because of its historic associations. He laid it aside inside a shed at Kirkhouse. The high scrap value of all its brass and copper components seems to have been too tempting, though, and they were apparently removed and sold during the 1840s. This left just the outline form of the locomotive, largely as preserved by the Science Museum.

Rocket remained something of a celebrity, however, and in 1851 serious consideration was given to putting it on display at the Great Exhibition in Hyde Park, London. It would have been shown alongside some of the latest locomotives to demonstrate how much progress had been made in just 22 years. It was taken back to Robert Stephenson's factory in Newcastle, where it was to be refurbished. When it was realised how many of the fittings had gone, however, the plan was abandoned, and *Rocket* was pushed out of the way into a corner of the factory, and left.

ELEVATIONS
OF THE
ROCKET
CONSTRUCTED BY
MESS.RS ROB.T STEPHENSON & CO
NEWCASTLE UPON TYNE
JULY 1829.

Figure 5.5 Rocket*'s final form when it was withdrawn from service in about 1840. The subsequent removal of many of the locomotive's copper and brass fittings has left the basic iron form that became part of the collections of the Science Museum. (National Railway Museum)*

5.4 *Museum exhibit*

There then followed 11 years of indecision regarding *Rocket*'s future, during which time its condition deteriorated. In 1862 its fortunes changed again. The Patent Office Museum in London was then developing a remarkable collection of machines that marked some of the important steps in the Industrial Revolution. Through the work of its energetic curator, Bennet Woodcroft, the museum sought out some of the oldest surviving locomotives, including *Rocket*. James Thompson had died by this time, but his widow Maria and her two sons agreed to donate it to the Patent Office Museum.

61

Robert Stephenson & Co. agreed to recondition *Rocket* to make it suitable for display in the museum. More than 30 years had passed since it had been made in the factory, however, and the company's personnel only had a vague idea of what it should look like. Without appreciating the significance of the several modifications that had been made during the locomotive's working life, they tried to re-create something of its original appearance at the Rainhill Trials. They made and fitted several erroneous components, including a set of carrying wheels at the rear that had apparently been transferred from a wagon. This resulted in an artefact that represented neither its original nor its end-of-service appearance. In this rather strange form it was put on display in the Patent Office Museum in South Kensington for visitors to admire (Figure 5.6).

Figure 5.6 Rocket *in the form in which it was first displayed at the Patent Office Museum in South Kensington. The several replacement components that had been fitted were a poor attempt to re-create the locomotive's appearance at the Rainhill Trials. The erroneous pieces were subsequently removed. (Science & Society Picture Library)*

The Patent Office Museum's artefacts, including *Rocket*, later passed into the Science Museum's collection. It was realised that its appearance was inaccurate and, in 1892, a first attempt was made towards an improvement. The second-hand carrying wheels were replaced with a new set, which remain fitted to the locomotive, although these wheels are still not an accurate representation of the original ones. One of the Museum's early curators, Ernest Forward, realised how inaccurate the rest of the restoration had been. He removed the other erroneous components, but did not succeed in his ambition to replace them with more accurate ones. Unfortunately, he also removed the buffer-beam extensions, which had been fitted at Kirkhouse for use with the chaldron wagons. These would have been an important reminder of *Rocket*'s later industrial work. Forward did, however, fit a replacement chimney in 1936, which remains with the locomotive.

Apart from only short periods during gallery improvements, *Rocket* has been exhibited in South Kensington ever since 1862. When the Museum's *Making the Modern World* gallery was being prepared in the late 1990s, the locomotive was loaned for several months for exhibition in Japan, the only time that it has left Britain. During 1999, it was placed on display at the National Railway Museum in York. It was during this year that the authors of this volume undertook a comprehensive investigation of *Rocket*, including detailed research into its history, on which this book is based. The locomotive returned to South Kensington for the opening of the new gallery in the summer of 2000.

Rocket is thus a remarkable and important survivor from the very dawn of the main-line railway era, and the beginning of mass travel in Britain and around the world. George and Robert Stephenson and other pioneers were all too aware of the importance of the steps they were taking. As one contemporary writer, Luke Hebert, observed:

Speed, despatch, distance, are still relative terms, but their meaning has been totally changed within a few months: what was quick, is now slow; what was distant is now near; and this change in our ideas will not be limited to the environs of Liverpool and Manchester, it will pervade society at large. A transition in our accustomed rate of travelling, from eight to ten miles per hour to fifteen or twenty (not to mention higher speeds), gives a new character to the whole internal trade and commerce of the country. A saving of time is a saving of money.

Index